Write the missing consonant to complete each word defined at the left. Use the letters *b, f, h, j, k, l, m, n, p, r, t, v, w,* and *y.*

1. Rich   ____ealthy

2. A long trip   ____ourney

3. A pot for boiling water   ____ettle

4. The time after now   ____uture

5. Empty   ____acant

6. The head of a city government   ____ayor

7. Meat often eaten for breakfast   baco____

8. A drink made from the juice of apples   cide____

9. A pail   bucke____

10. A list of events   progra____

11. Twelve of something   doze____

12. The fast run of a horse   gallo____

13. To disappear   va____ish

14. A person who makes bread, cakes, and pies   ba____er

15. A mixture of green vegetables   sa____ad

16. A deep valley with steep sides   can____on

17. The taste of something   fla____or

18. A covering to protect the head   hel____et

In the following group, the last letter in each word is the same as the first letter in the next word.

1. A person who flies an airplane   ____i____o____

2. A spring flower   ____u____i____

3. A student   ____u____i____

4. A sour, juicy fruit   ____e____o____

5. Not at any time   ____e____e____

Some consonants have more than one sound.

c *k* as in *cut*
      s as in *city*
      sh (with *i*) as in *special*

g *g* as in *geese*
      j as in *giant*

s *s* as in *salt*
      z as in *rose*
      sh (with *u*) as in *sure*
      zh (with *u*) as in *treasure*

t *t* as in *tag*
      ch (with *u*) as in *fortune*
      ch (with *i*) as in *question*
      sh (with *i*) as in *station*

Above each underlined letter or letter combination, write the symbol or symbols that stand for its sound.

1. huge	12. official	23. measure	34. vicious
2. yourself	13. design	24. ancient	35. faucet
3. deserve	14. pleasure	25. sugar	36. rescue
4. vinegar	15. rage	26. introduce	37. creature
5. usual	16. cheese	27. patient	38. carriage
6. ability	17. oxygen	28. precious	39. ancestor
7. future	18. bargain	29. situation	40. gesture
8. chocolate	19. tumble	30. musician	41. hesitate
9. orange	20. hinge	31. increase	42. cautious
10. museum	21. regular	32. action	43. conversation
11. icy	22. ridge	33. vacation	44. society

2

In some words, two or three consonants come together and their sounds are blended. These are called *consonant blends*. The most common blends are *br, cr, dr, fr, gr, pr, tr, bl, cl, fl, gl, pl, st, sp, sc, sk, sw, tw, sm, sn, scr, spl, spr, str,* and *squ.*

Complete each word below by adding one of the above blends to the letters shown.

____ ____ift	____ ____een	____ ____oke	____ ____ept
____ ____ift	____ ____ ____een	____ ____ ____oke	____ ____ept
____ ____ing	____ ____ame	____ ____ell	____ ____in
____ ____ing	____ ____ame	____ ____ell	____ ____in
____ ____ing	____ ____ame	____ ____ell	____ ____in

Write the missing blend to complete each word defined at the left. Use the blends listed at the top of the page.

1. The cost of something   ____ ____ice

2. To sparkle   ____ ____inkle

3. To press together   ____ ____ ____eeze

4. A nail on the toe of an animal   ____ ____aw

5. To break into pieces   ____ ____ ____it

6. A squeaking sound   ____ ____eak

7. To growl sharply   ____ ____arl

8. To welcome   ____ ____eet

9. Something used for weighing   ____ ____ale

10. To take long steps when walking   ____ ____ ____ide

11. To hang down   ____ ____oop

12. A person who travels to get new information   ex____ ____orer

13. Ran away   ____ ____ed

14. To use words to tell about something   de ____ ____ ____ibe

15. To move smoothly   ____ ____ide

In some words, two consonants come together. They form one special sound that is different from either of the two individual consonant sounds. These are called *consonant digraphs.* The most common consonant digraphs are *ch, ck, ng, sh, th,* and *wh.*

Complete each word by adding one of the above digraphs to the letters shown.

____ ____ick	____ ____ere	____ ____ief	____ ____en
____ ____ick	____ ____ere	____ ____ief	____ ____en
pa____ ____	sti____ ____	tra____ ____	wi____ ____
pa____ ____	sti____ ____	tra____ ____	wi____ ____

Circle the word in each pair which is defined at the left.

1.	To have a hope for	wing	wish
2.	A male ruler	kick	king
3.	To cut into small pieces	chop	shop
4.	A footprint	trash	track
5.	A low, crying sound	whine	shine
6.	Not at all fat	chin	thin
7.	A kind of tree	birth	birch
8.	A bag	sack	sash
9.	The wound of a bee	stick	sting
10.	Picked out	chose	those
11.	To make quiet	hush	hung
12.	A male deer	buck	bush
13.	A slap	smash	smack
14.	To excite	shrill	thrill
15.	To strike with a whip	lack	lash
16.	To hold on to	cling	click
17.	The grain used to make flour	cheat	wheat
18.	To talk in a quick way	shatter	chatter

4

Consonant blends and consonant digraphs may be found at the beginning of words, in the middle, or at the end.

In the paragraph below, circle the words containing consonant blends and underline those containing consonant digraphs. (Do not underline the word *the*.)

Last winter our family had all the popcorn we could eat. The summer before that, we raised our own vegetables. Our backyard in the city is tiny. So Mom and Dad paid to use a garden plot in the county park. Often we stayed to work on it until dusk. We each used a shovel and some other tools. Many nights we took a picnic dinner along with us. In May, little sprouts could be seen. Only the radishes were ready. But by July, we had a garden full of beautiful vegetables. My favorites were the watermelons, the best I've ever tasted. I liked the popcorn, too. Winter nights didn't seem complete unless we ate some. When we discuss if we'd like a garden again, we all agree.

Write the words containing consonant blends and consonant digraphs in the correct column. Show the position of the blend or digraph by writing the word in the correct row.

	Consonant Blends	Consonant Digraphs
Beginning	_____ _____ _____	_____ _____ _____
Middle	_____ _____ _____	_____ _____ _____
End	_____ _____	_____ _____

The consonant digraph *ch* has three sounds.

ch—*choice*   k—*echo*   sh—*mustache*

The consonant digraph *th* has two sounds.

th—*thick*   TH—*this*

On the line in front of each word, write the symbol or symbols that stand for the sound of the underlined letters.

_____ 1. au<u>th</u>or

_____ 2. monar<u>ch</u>

_____ 3. ba<u>th</u>e

_____ 4. para<u>ch</u>ute

_____ 5. sou<u>th</u>

_____ 6. pin<u>ch</u>

_____ 7. weal<u>th</u>

_____ 8. <u>th</u>us

_____ 9. <u>ch</u>aracter

_____ 10. <u>ch</u>urn

_____ 11. whe<u>th</u>er

_____ 12. <u>th</u>irsty

_____ 13. <u>th</u>ose

_____ 14. an<u>ch</u>or

_____ 15. bo<u>th</u>er

_____ 16. <u>ch</u>ill

_____ 17. ma<u>ch</u>ine

_____ 18. ex<u>ch</u>ange

_____ 19. mou<u>th</u>ful

_____ 20. a<u>ch</u>e

_____ 21. en<u>ch</u>ant

• •

The sound of *sh* is represented by five spellings.

s—*sure*   sh—*shy*   ch—*machine*   ci—*special*   ti—*mention*

On the line in front of each word, write the letter or letters that stand for the sound of *sh* in the word.

_____ 1. precious

_____ 2. ashore

_____ 3. cautious

_____ 4. fashion

_____ 5. motion

_____ 6. ancient

_____ 7. mustache

_____ 8. astonish

_____ 9. sugar

_____ 10. patience

_____ 11. shelter

_____ 12. delicious

_____ 13. parachute

_____ 14. attention

_____ 15. official

_____ 16. relation

_____ 17. vanish

_____ 18. musician

_____ 19. station

_____ 20. situation

_____ 21. shawl

Sounds of **ch** and **th**; Sounds Representing **sh**

Each of the following words contains a short vowel sound.

ă	ĕ	ĭ	ŏ	ŭ
cap	jet	tin	sob	rug

In the paragraph below, circle each word that has a short vowel sound in it.

I like to fish. All that I need is a rod, a line, fresh bait, plus a weight to hold the bait down. The rest is easy. First I gather the worms. I find a quiet place at a nearby pond for my fun. I drop the line before I prop the rod by a rock. At times I lie on the grassy bank to wait for a nibble on the line. Each season I check around for a new spot. But I also keep a few special places to myself. My uncle can't seem to figure me out. He didn't know girls liked such things. I can't explain, either. I just like to fish.

Write each circled word next to the letter that stands for its short vowel sound. If the same word is circled more than once, write it only one time.

ă _____ _____ _____

ĕ _____ _____ _____

ĭ _____ _____ _____

ŏ _____ _____ _____

ŭ _____ _____ _____

The sound of long *a* is represented by these five spelling patterns.

ea—*gr*e*a*t   ai—*p*a*id*   ey—*they*   ay—*hay*   ei—*eight*

Long *a* is also represented by another spelling pattern.

a/consonant/silent *e*—*cave, gate*

In the paragraphs below, circle the words with the long *a* sound.

For my birthday, my parents gave me a stamp album. I check all our mail now. Our neighbors save stamps for me, too. You can also buy stamps from faraway countries at a hobby shop. I have to pay for them myself. I trade stamps with other collectors, too.

My friends collect all kinds of things. Mary collects rocks. Some are plain, but others are quite beautiful. Eduardo collects butterflies in a case. He is careful not to break their wings when he mounts them. Rochelle has been collecting coins for eight months. Her collection already contains an unusual 1914 penny. Phan has a great collection of baseball cards. And his dad collects old toy trains and planes.

On the line in front of each definition, write the correct circled word from the paragraphs above.

_____   **1.** People who live near one another

_____   **2.** Connected lines of cars pulled along a track

_____   **3.** To put aside for the future

_____   **4.** Common or ordinary

_____   **5.** Machines which have wings and fly

_____   **6.** Includes

_____   **7.** To exchange one thing for another

_____   **8.** A container to put things in

_____   **9.** Distant

_____   **10.** A game played with a ball and bat

The sound of long *e* is represented by these seven spelling patterns.

e—*w<u>e</u>*   ea—*<u>lea</u>p*   ei—*c<u>ei</u>ling*   y—*bus<u>y</u>*

ee—*w<u>ee</u>k*   ie—*ch<u>ie</u>f*   ey—*donk<u>ey</u>*

In the paragraph below, circle the words with the long *e* sound.

Think of a very large object that is shaped like a giant cigar and travels in the sky. It can carry as many as fifty passengers. It is a blimp. This airship is lifted into the air by a special gas that is lighter than air. Some of the old blimps were up to eight hundred feet long. They could reach a speed of seventy miles an hour. Blimps were once a popular means of travel. Then travelers received news of several bad accidents, and the passenger service ended. Today, some experts believe that blimps should be tried again. They think blimps can be flown safely now. Other key reasons are also important. Blimps run quietly. They need only a small landing field. And they cost less money to run than airplanes.

On the line in front of each definition, write the correct circled word from the paragraph above.

_____   **1.** To think of as true

_____   **2.** A cleared piece of land

_____   **3.** Important, main

_____   **4.** Half of one hundred

_____   **5.** Causes of something

_____   **6.** Without accident or harm

_____   **7.** Something used to pay costs

_____   **8.** A measure of length

_____   **9.** A measure of movement

_____   **10.** Got

The sound of long *i* is represented by these three spelling patterns.

ie—*t**ie***   igh—*t**igh**t*   y—*sp**y***

Long *i* is also represented by another spelling pattern.

i/consonant/silent *e—mine, bike*

In the paragraph below, circle the words with the long *i* sound.

Some types of popular beliefs have to do with luck. There are people who believe that you shouldn't walk under a ladder or open an umbrella inside a house. One of the most famous of these beliefs has to do with the number thirteen. Many people thought about it during our third moon flight. The spaceship was called Apollo 13. The ride into space began quite well on a bright Saturday in April of 1970. The captain was Jim Lovell. Everything went fine for two days. Then came word of an accident on the ship 206,000 miles from Earth. It happened on April 13. People were frightened for Lovell and his crew. Everyone feared that they might die. The world was delighted when they arrived home safely at last. It would be a lie, though, to say that the accident didn't cause people to think again about the number thirteen.

On the line in front of each definition, write the correct circled word from the paragraph above.

_____   **1.** Afraid

_____   **2.** An untrue statement

_____   **3.** Pleased and happy

_____   **4.** To stop living

_____   **5.** Could

_____   **6.** Reached a place

_____   **7.** A trip in which a person is carried on something

_____   **8.** A trip through the air

_____   **9.** Certain kinds

The sound of long *o* is represented by these five spelling patterns.

o—*no*   oe—*toe*   oa—*float*   ow—*blow*   ough—*though*

Long *o* is also represented by another spelling pattern.

o/consonant/silent *e*—*hope, drove*

In the paragraph below, circle the words with the long *o* sound.

Do you usually have a snack when you get home? Many people go straight to the refrigerator. They look for a bottle of soft drink. Or they stand on their tiptoes to reach a special treat. They look for sweets, like candy or doughnuts. These snack foods are loaded with sugar, though. They may taste good, but they aren't good for you. Too much sugar can ruin teeth and cause weight problems. It's easy to learn to choose snacks that aren't so bad for you. Try drinks that are low in sugar. Or make a float with milk and fruit. Try eating fresh fruit or roasted peanuts. You can also mix the fresh fruit slices with the nuts for a tasty treat. Whenever you eat good snack foods, you'll know you have done your body a favor.

On the line in front of each definition, write the correct circled word from the paragraph above.

_____   **1.** Too

_____   **2.** To understand

_____   **3.** Less than usual

_____   **4.** A sweet drink containing fruit or ice cream

_____   **5.** Filled

_____   **6.** The place where you live

_____   **7.** Cooked in an oven

_____   **8.** Small cakes shaped like a ring

_____   **9.** Even so

_____   **10.** The opposite of "stop"

Each of these vowel sounds is represented by more than one spelling.

ū—m<u>u</u>le, f<u>ew</u>   oo—z<u>oo</u>, thr<u>ough</u>, n<u>ew</u>, s<u>ui</u>t, bl<u>ue</u>

The letters *oo* also have the sound of o͝o in *book*.

In each group of words below, circle the two words with the same vowel sound.

1. cube	rude	view	**11.** zoo	flew	found
2. hook	brook	troop	**12.** wood	bruise	grew
3. blue	trout	group	**13.** drew	chew	shook
4. look	school	crew	**14.** through	mule	noon
5. few	cute	true	**15.** doubt	mood	scoop
6. mouse	smooth	flute	**16.** fruit	guide	blew
7. juice	quit	tooth	**17.** good	clue	loose
8. cook	goose	pool	**18.** shoot	too	loud
9. stood	threw	soup	**19.** shout	gloom	choose
10. took	soon	good	**20.** pew	scout	huge

In each sentence below, circle the two words with the same vowel sound. Use only those vowel spellings listed at the top of the page.

1. A cool fruit salad is perfect on a hot summer day.

2. Only a few of those huge logs will be cut and shaped into chairs.

3. Water those blue flowers, and they will not droop.

4. I placed worms on the hook and then dropped the line into the brook.

5. We viewed a film about the use of soybeans.

6. The detectives searched the crew for clues that could help solve the mystery.

7. After the storm, a group of children threw snowballs at each other.

8. The astronauts made a loop around the moon and then came home.

9. Before the crook went into the bank, he pulled a hood over his head.

A single vowel followed by *r* is neither long nor short. The *r* gives the vowel a different sound. When *or* follows *w*, it also has the sound heard in *work*.

ar	**er**	**ir**	**or**	**ur**
p<u>ar</u>t	s<u>er</u>ve	d<u>ir</u>t	f<u>or</u>k, w<u>or</u>k	c<u>ur</u>l

Complete each sentence with one of the words below the blank.

1. Angie _____ her elbow when she fell off her skateboard.
   (hurt, hut)

2. One of the most frightening sea animals is the _____.
   (shack, shark)

3. Beth's long _____ got caught in the elevator door.
   (skirt, skit)

4. Sean tied the package carefully with heavy _____.
   (cod, cord)

5. By crawling through the earth, a _____ helps the soil to breathe.
   (wore, worm)

6. Cover your mouth when you sneeze, or you'll spread _____.
   (gems, germs)

● ●

The spelling *ear* has three sounds.

1. h<u>ear</u>   2. b<u>ear</u>   3. <u>ear</u>n

Complete each sentence with one of the words below the blank.
Then write the numeral of the key word that has the same sound.

1. Did you _____ the sirens last night? ____
   (heal, hear)

2. I would like to _____ to speak Spanish. ____
   (lean, learn)

3. Toni likes to _____ sandals in the summer. ____
   (wear, weak)

4. Ripe, sweet _____ are my favorite fruit. ____
   (peaks, pears)

If *i* is followed by *ld, nd,* or *gh*, it usually has the long vowel sound.

If *o* is followed by *ld, lt,* or *st*, it usually has the long vowel sound.

knight

ghost

In the paragraph below, circle all the words with a long *i* or long *o* sound.

Last weekend, Rita gave a costume party. Some people looked frightful. However, a gentle ghost with a mild manner didn't shock anyone. Other people dressed funny. A wild colt had canes for its front legs. Jerome came as a gold bird. With his loose feathers, he looked ready to molt. Jack Frost was there, too. He actually made me feel cold. After everyone saw everyone else, we guessed who was behind each mask. Lee got a new CD for getting the most right. Then we had a treasure hunt for nuts and apples. We could keep whatever we could find. All in all, it was a great party.

On the line in front of each definition, write the correct circled word from the paragraph above.

_____ 1. The opposite of lose

_____ 2. A young horse

_____ 3. Very scary

_____ 4. More than the others

_____ 5. The opposite of tame

_____ 6. Extremely chilly

_____ 7. A valuable metal

_____ 8. Correct

_____ 9. A make-believe creature

14

Sounds of ***ild, ind, igh, old, olt,*** and ***ost***

The letter *y* may represent a vowel sound or a consonant sound. When it stands for a vowel sound, it has the sound of long *i* or long *e*.

Consonant y—*yes* (y)   Vowel y—*fry* (ī) or *city* (ē)

In the paragraph below, circle the words in which *y* is a consonant and underline those in which it is a vowel.

I've never seen more than a few sparrows in our yard. Even so, I decided to build a birdfeeder. After I hung it on a tree branch, I waited nearby to see if some birds would come along. The sparrows came first. Before long, a noisy mockingbird appeared. It chased off the other birds. It also chased our puppy, which ran off with an unhappy yelp. Later, a beautiful redbird decided to fly over and try the feeder. As he ate, he sang a pretty song. His mate sang a reply. Next a bright yellow bird stopped by. It looked like a canary. It seemed young and shy. Mom said it was a goldfinch. I keep the feeder filled with plenty of seed. All year long, I'll be able to watch the birds that come to our backyard.

Write each circled and underlined word in the correct column.

Consonant y	**y — long i**	**y — long e**
_____	_____	_____
_____	_____	_____
_____	_____	_____
_____	_____	_____
_____	_____	_____

The vowel spelling *ea* has more than one sound.

ē	**ā**	**ĕ**
s<u>ea</u>l	st<u>ea</u>k	thr<u>ea</u>d

In the paragraph below, circle each word with the vowel spelling *ea*.

Every living creature is special in one way or another. Ostriches are great runners, and penguins are good swimmers. Both birds have feathers, but neither can fly. Giant pandas are quite large, and yet they are like raccoons in some ways. Both animals have strong claws and very sharp teeth. But pandas eat plants instead of meat. Then there are anteaters, which love to feast on an anthill. Beavers have tails that look like paddles. They work hard while otters seem to live just to have fun. They get their pleasure sliding down a mud bank into a lake. Bats are dreadful looking animals. Although many of them can't see very well, they always know where they're heading. Finally, there are the whales. These animals live underwater. Every once in a while, they take a break to come up for a breath of air. Even the whales know that they aren't fish.

Write each circled word in the correct column.

ē	**ā**	**ĕ**
_____	_____	_____
_____	_____	_____
_____		_____
_____		_____
_____		_____

Each of these sounds is represented by two different spellings.

ou	**ō**	**oi**
loud	*though*	*joy*
town	*bowl*	*join*

In the paragraph below, circle those words with the *ow* spelling, underline those with the *ou* spelling, and box those with the *oi* or *oy* spelling.

    Today more and more people are talking about solar power. Even many boys and girls have used it. When they burn a hole in paper with a magnifying glass, they are using solar energy. That's using it as a toy, though. Scientists are interested in knowing more. They want to use the sun's energy to cook food and boil water. They'd like to learn how to heat a house with it. They want to warm buildings when clouds fill the sky, snow covers the ground, and the north wind blows. Other kinds of fuel, like oil and coal, are running low. So scientists see the sun as the best fuel choice for the future. The next time the sun shines in a nearby window, think solar.

Write each circled, underlined, and boxed word in the correct column.

ou	**ō**	**oi**
_____	_____	_____
_____	_____	_____
_____	_____	_____
_____	_____	_____
_____	_____	

The following single vowels and vowel combinations sometimes have the same sound. This sound is represented by the symbol ô.

ô	ô	ô	ô	ô
w<u>a</u>lk	c<u>or</u>n	f<u>au</u>lt	dr<u>aw</u>	br<u>ough</u>t

In each group of words below, circle the two words with the same vowel sound. Underline the letters that stand for the ô sound. Use only those vowels listed above.

1. yawn	wall	young		**11.** round	haunt	walk
2. through	off	taught		**12.** dawn	fault	rolled
3. caught	soup	fought		**13.** tall	bat	hawk
4. call	sought	mop		**14.** porch	lawn	rock
5. loud	dog	paw		**15.** show	frog	shawl
6. cause	cloth	should		**16.** talk	claw	rough
7. frost	most	small		**17.** group	ought	jaw
8. knot	bald	log		**18.** squawk	ton	born
9. fall	tough	haul		**19.** glad	all	crawl
10. hall	stop	pause		**20.** raw	cost	ghost

In each sentence below, circle the two words with the ô sound. Use only those vowel spellings listed at the top of the page.

1. It doesn't really matter whether someone is short or tall.

2. I saw the ball roll into the bushes, but now I can't find it.

3. Pedro brought salt to the picnic, but not pepper.

4. Allen thought the accident was his fault.

5. Cindy bought her sister a shawl as a gift.

6. The children paused as they entered the haunted funhouse.

7. You ought to be careful when lighting a torch.

8. I hauled at least six boxes of bricks over the lawn to build a new fireplace.

9. Hawks and bald eagles are members of the same bird family.

18

The vowel spelling *ou* has more than one sound.

ō	ô	ü	ŭ	ou
d<u>ough</u>	br<u>ough</u>t	y<u>ou</u>	t<u>ou</u>ch	h<u>ou</u>se

In the paragraph below, circle each word with the vowel spelling *ou*.

Last Saturday my cousin and I went to a public sale in the
country. It was held outside, so we brought lawn chairs with us. We
were the youngest people there. Sometimes it can be tough for
youths in a group so large. But we soon understood what all the
loud shouting meant. Although there were thousands of things to
buy, we bought only a few. After a while, we walked through the
crowd to find some food. We each had chicken soup and a
doughnut. We never thought we'd stay long. But it was such fun
that we decided we ought to stay the whole day.

Write each circled word next to the symbol that stands for the
sound of *ou* in the word.

ō   _____

        _____

ô   _____   _____

        _____   _____

ü   _____   _____

        _____   _____

ŭ   _____   _____

        _____   _____

ou   _____   _____

        _____   _____

The letters *qu* represent the sound of *kw*.

 quilt

The letters *gu* represent the sound of *g*.

 guest

The letters *gh* and *ph* sometimes represent the sound of *f*.

 rough

 elephant

In the paragraph below, circle each word with one of these letter combinations.

Guess what Dad came home with last week—CB radio equipment for the house. First he read the guide for it. Then he showed us how to use it. At first the radio was quiet. Later there were many noisy squeaks and squeals. We corrected that quickly enough. Now our CB headquarters is filled with much fun and laughter. I really have to laugh when I hear other people's handles. One person is called Daffy Dolphin. Another is King's Guard. Dad calls himself Tongue Twister. That radio is like having guests in the house. It's often better than a telephone. It has even helped me become more familiar with the geography of our area. I can guarantee you that a CB is a good buddy.

Write each circled word in the correct column.

kw	g	f
_____	_____	_____
_____	_____	_____
_____	_____	_____
_____	_____	_____
_____	_____	_____

20

The ending *-ed* has three sounds. When it is added to some words, it forms a separate syllable.

ed—*lift**ed***   d—*cheer**ed***   t—*rush**ed***

In the paragraph below, circle the words in which the ending *-ed* has been added.

Many doctors and scientists have discovered ways to save lives. One person who stands out is Charles Drew. Charles grew up in a poor section of Washington, D.C. He enjoyed sports and learned quickly. In high school, Drew played in four different sports and still succeeded in getting good grades. He then attended college and medical school, where he earned high marks. After Drew finished medical school, he returned to Washington to teach. Later, while working in a hospital, Dr. Drew expressed an interest in studying blood. He worked and developed a way to store blood until it was needed. This had never been done before. It was important because World War II had just started. People wounded in battle needed blood. Drew's discovery has helped millions of other people, too. Sadly, his own life ended early. His car crashed one night in 1950. We can be thankful Charles Drew gave so much while he was alive.

Write each circled word in the correct column. Divide into syllables the words in which *-ed* adds a syllable.

ed	d	t
_____	_____	_____
_____	_____	_____
_____	_____	_____
_____	_____	_____
_____	_____	_____

Many words look alike except for a few letters.

moan—moon   palace—place

Complete each sentence with one of the words below the blank.

1. The highway followed the path of a Native American _____.
(trial, trail)

2. Steam rose from the bowl of hot _____.
(soup, soap)

3. Darlene waited on the sidewalk for the light to _____.
(chance, change)

4. The _____ gas station is about eleven miles away.
(closet, closest)

5. An _____ in his side forced Leroy out of the race.
(arch, ache)

6. Pepe likes to eat _____ with his eggs.
(sausages, savages)

7. The car _____ on the ice and spun completely around.
(skipped, skidded)

8. In which _____ were your grandparents born?
(nation, nature)

9. After each baseball game, Hiko _____ about his hits.
(beasts, boasts)

10. Please _____ me to return my library books today.
(remain, remind)

11. The new band uniforms have a white _____ down each pant leg.
(stripe, stride)

12. During the _____, Sandy played a solo on the trumpet.
(concern, concert)

13. At the bottom of this steep hill, the road _____ sharply to the right.
(curves, carves)

14. Seat belts are an important safety _____ on cars.
(future, feature)

22

In each row, circle the words that contain the sound shown at the beginning of the row.

1. **k**	carve	echo	cement	arch	cub
2. **s**	base	chose	sugar	cider	solid
3. **sh**	coach	official	motion	lash	sure
4. **z**	wisdom	muscle	custom	design	observe
5. **zh**	usual	pleasure	desire	result	television
6. **g**	gesture	freight	fog	gym	gulp
7. **j**	ledge	original	regular	gently	urge
8. **t**	captain	within	actor	protest	latch
9. **ch**	mustache	pinch	future	anchor	chirp
10. **th**	health	thee	truth	author	thirsty
11. **ŦH**	bathe	booth	thus	smooth	warmth
12. **y**	cycle	canyon	navy	style	yelp
13. **f**	dolphin	height	paragraph	tough	dough
14. **kw**	tongue	question	quit	equal	guide
15. **t**	touched	ruined	grounded	gripped	shocked
16. **d**	limped	blamed	sealed	mapped	carved
17. **ed**	posted	peeled	aided	shifted	vanished

In each row, circle the words that contain the same vowel sound.

1. death   guest   breathe   bet   scent   rein

2. known   prop   lodge   cord   rod   through

3. bunch   churn   snug   tough   rude   blood

4. bait   hey   leash   clank   tray   weigh

5. pearl   speed   heap   wealth   chief   seize

6. file   veil   guide   height   grind   sink

7. cost   boast   frown   shown   post   stole

8. view   cube   mud   growl   curve   huge

9. bloom   youth   bruise   dough   clue   flood

10. chart   stare   ward   barge   shark   arch

11. glare   worth   blurt   fern   twirl   wore

12. swarm   scarce   pear   starve   flare   prayer

13. smear   rare   mere   stern   oar   fear

14. port   torch   work   sore   score   court

15. ought   mount   rough   owe   trout   scowl

16. boil   joy   choice   sly   doubt   tow

17. salt   boss   haul   hound   grown   frog

A contraction is made from two or more words written together. An apostrophe (') represents the letter or letters that have been left out.

Write the contraction for each of these word pairs.

1. I will _____   7. he will _____

2. you are _____   8. has not _____

3. should not _____   9. we have _____

4. here is _____   10. she has _____

5. he had _____   11. you had _____

6. we are _____   12. you would _____

Write the words that were used to form each of these contractions.

1. I'm _____   7. he's _____

2. you'll _____   8. we'll _____

3. don't _____   9. there's _____

4. you've _____   10. hadn't _____

5. aren't _____   11. she'd _____

6. we'd _____   12. I'll _____

Complete each sentence with one of the words below the line.

1. _____ the hammer Dad needed this morning.
   (Here's, Hears)

2. The front _____ on my bike is bent.
   (wheel, we'll)

3. When _____ sick, try to get some extra sleep.
   (your, you're)

4. _____ no glue left to finish my art project.
   (Theirs, There's)

5. Tom will win the race if _____ just keep running.
   (he'll, heel)

6. If we want to be on time, _____ better leave now.
   (weed, we'd)

A compound word is formed by joining two or more small words.
Join the words in each list and write the compound words on the lines.

gold	shield	1. _____
wind	port	2. _____
air	house	3. _____
drug	quarters	4. _____
some	fish	5. _____
light	shore	6. _____
head	road	7. _____
sea	store	8. _____
rail	how	9. _____

Sometimes a compound word is written as one word, sometimes as separate words, and sometimes with a hyphen connecting the small words.

eyebrow   *high school*   *tongue-tied*

Circle the compound word in each sentence below. Then write its separate parts on the line in front of the sentence.

_____ 1. The clowns put on their make-up and took their places.

_____ 2. During the art festival, the sidewalk was filled with people.

_____ 3. Hank Aaron hit 756 home runs during his long career.

_____ 4. My brother is the only left-handed person in our family.

_____ 5. Every Saturday, Carol baby-sits for her little cousin.

_____ 6. Terri screeched when she hit her funny bone on the desk.

_____ 7. The framework of the building looked like a giant steel web.

_____ 8. The huge waves smashed the beach at high tide.

_____ 9. Playing in the sunshine helps people stay healthy.

_____ 10. Last year, earthquakes hit the southern part of the state.

_____ 11. At camp, we slept in a cabin with bunk beds.

26

Plurals are words which name more than one. They are formed in several ways.

1. Add -s to most words. *cab—cab**s***	2. Add -es to words that end in s, x, sh, ch, or tch. *leash—leash**es***
3. Change y to i and add -es to words that end in a consonant plus y. *duty—dut**ies***	4. Add -s to words that end in a vowel plus y. *tray—tray**s***
5. Change f to v and add -s or -es to words that end in f or fe. *leaf—lea**ves***	6. If a word ends in a consonant plus o, usually -es is added. If it ends in a vowel plus o, usually -s is added. *potato—potato**es*** *radio—radio**s***

On the first line after each word below, write the numeral of the sentence above that tells how to form its plural. On the second line, write the plural form.

1. sash ___ _____

2. tomato ___ _____

3. antler ___ _____

4. journey ___ _____

5. life ___ _____

6. victory ___ _____

7. chorus ___ _____

8. knife ___ _____

9. bully ___ _____

10. elbow ___ _____

11. calf ___ _____

12. rodeo ___ _____

13. ditch ___ _____

14. subway ___ _____

15. lasso ___ _____

16. guppy ___ _____

17. half ___ _____

18. ray ___ _____

19. mosquito ___ _____

20. tax ___ _____

21. diary ___ _____

22. zero ___ _____

23. variety ___ _____

24. melody ___ _____

The possessive form of a word shows ownership.

1. Add *'s* to words that name one person or animal.	2. Add an apostrophe *(')* to plural words that end in *s.*	3. Add *'s* to plural words that do not end in *s.*
a mayor<u>'s</u> office	the rats<u>'</u> nest	the geese<u>'s</u> feathers

In each sentence below, underline the phrase that can be rewritten to show possession. On the first line, write the numeral of the sentence above that tells how to make the word possessive. On the second line, write the possessive form.

1. Some babies can drink only the milk of goats.   _____ _____

2. The homes of the mice were behind the warm stove.   _____ _____

3. In many ways, the difficult job of cowhands can be exciting.   _____ _____

4. The cheers of the audience rang through the hall.   _____ _____

5. Snow covered the tent of the explorer.   _____ _____

6. The lines of the fishermen hung over the boat.   _____ _____

7. All along the creek, dams of beavers could be seen.   _____ _____

8. The ancestors of my friends came from Italy.   _____ _____

9. The wool of the lamb was soft and fluffy.   _____ _____

10. The crown of the king rested on a pillow next to the throne.   _____ _____

11. I have to admire the courage of policewomen.   _____ _____

12. The expressions on the faces of the children showed their love of magic.   _____ _____

13. Sara is the name of my cousin, too!   _____ _____

14. The mother of the kittens was nowhere to be seen.   _____ _____

The spellings of some words are not changed before a suffix is added.

ant + s = ants   clank + ing = clanking   leaf + y = leafy
arch + es = arches   mild + er = milder   slight + ly = slightly
bloom + ed = bloomed   odd + est = oddest   peace + ful = peaceful

In each sentence below, underline the word whose spelling was
not changed before the suffix was added. Then write its root
word on the line in front of the sentence.

_____ 1. Playing with fire can have a serious result.

_____ 2. The giraffe is the tallest animal in the world.

_____ 3. A mountain climber must always be alert for danger.

_____ 4. Jim Thorpe may have been the greatest athlete of all time.

_____ 5. Be sure the ashes from the fire are cold before we leave.

_____ 6. The helicopter hovered near the crash area.

_____ 7. Ellen came home promptly for supper.

_____ 8. Lisa did not complain about the painful cut on her arm.

_____ 9. My mother is lonely when Dad is away on a business trip.

_____ 10. Mark was squirming in his seat through the entire speech.

_____ 11. Who put these pebbles in the bottom of the fishbowl?

_____ 12. The carton was stuffed into the closet.

_____ 13. The rocket blasted into space toward the planet Mars.

_____ 14. A sneaky fox got into the chicken house last night.

_____ 15. Bigfoot is seven feet tall and very hairy.

_____ 16. The best ride in the park is the super coaster.

_____ 17. Millie is building a car for the soap box derby.

_____ 18. The river is rougher today than it was yesterday.

In some words, the final consonant is doubled before a suffix is added.

$$trip + p + ed = tripped \qquad star + r + y = starry$$
$$plot + t + ing = plotting \qquad hit + t + er = hitter$$

In each sentence below, underline the word in which the final consonant was doubled before the suffix was added. Then write its root word on the line in front of the sentence.

_____   **1.** Denise is the best swimmer on her team.

_____   **2.** Yesterday was sunny, but today it may rain.

_____   **3.** Larry admitted that he broke the window.

_____   **4.** Fortunately, the batter ducked out of the way of the fast ball.

_____   **5.** Mapping out our trip across the country was fun.

_____   **6.** My dog has a long, furry coat.

_____   **7.** Skipping flat rocks across the water is easy.

_____   **8.** The cookie cutter is in the bottom drawer.

_____   **9.** Leo bragged all day about the fish he caught.

_____   **10.** It was so foggy that I couldn't see the road.

_____   **11.** A dripping faucet wastes a lot of water.

_____   **12.** Since Jean never gives up, she can't be called a quitter.

_____   **13.** The beavers dammed up the stream with small trees.

_____   **14.** The dolphin flipped out of the water to catch the fish.

_____   **15.** The topping on the cake was made of sugar, nuts, and syrup.

_____   **16.** Frogs make funny noises at night.

_____   **17.** As the candle burned down, the room became dimmer.

_____   **18.** The bread popped out of the toaster and onto the floor.

Doubling the Final Consonant Before Adding a Suffix

In most words that end in a consonant plus *y*, the *y* is changed to *i* before a suffix is added.

$$duty + i + es = duties \qquad sturdy + i + est = sturdiest$$
$$bury + i + ed = buried \qquad clumsy + i + ly = clumsily$$
$$icy + i + er = icier \qquad beauty + i + ful = beautiful$$

In each sentence below, underline the word in which the *y* was changed to *i* before the suffix was added. Then write the word without its suffix on the line in front of the sentence.

_____ **1.** No place is drier than the desert.

_____ **2.** The football bounced crazily across the field.

_____ **3.** The batteries in Denny's flashlight were dead.

_____ **4.** Teresa shouted angrily when Marty pulled her hair.

_____ **5.** My grandfather was the liveliest person at the picnic.

_____ **6.** I can't decide which of the two movies was scarier.

_____ **7.** Each time that river overflows, three counties are flooded.

_____ **8.** These are the juiciest peaches I've ever eaten.

_____ **9.** Who supplied the prizes at the Halloween party?

_____ **10.** Many people live in large cities like New York.

_____ **11.** I have never been thirstier than I was after that long hike.

_____ **12.** Mr. Thompson seemed worried because the bus was late.

_____ **13.** When Kay was done writing, she recopied her poem neatly.

_____ **14.** I think the straw hat is more beautiful than the white one.

_____ **15.** The kitten purrs happily when it is petted.

_____ **16.** The bright fire made the room seem cozier.

_____ **17.** Fresh corn is plentiful at the end of summer.

_____ **18.** That is the tiniest dog I've ever seen.

Changing **y** to **i** Before Adding a Suffix

In words that end in silent *e*, the *e* is usually dropped before a suffix is added.

welcom*e* + ed = welcomed   cut*e* + er = cuter   ros*e* + y = rosy
          judg*e* + ing = judging   pur*e* + est = purest

In each sentence below, underline the word in which the final
silent *e* was dropped before the suffix was added. Then write its
root word on the line in front of the sentence.

_____ **1.** Is San Francisco closer to Portland or Los Angeles?

_____ **2.** The North Star sparkled brightly in the night sky.

_____ **3.** The family awoke before the smoky fire got too big.

_____ **4.** The plane circled the airport for an hour before it landed.

_____ **5.** The first problem on the page is usually the simplest.

_____ **6.** Many whaling ships sailed out of New England ports.

_____ **7.** The largest of the fifty states is Alaska.

_____ **8.** Mel raced through the park on her bike.

_____ **9.** The soda was so bubbly that Ted began to sneeze.

_____ **10.** The police were very puzzled about the robbery.

_____ **11.** When you are leaving, remember to use the side door.

_____ **12.** Why is the owl said to be the wisest animal?

_____ **13.** The sidewalk is icy, so watch your step.

_____ **14.** A giant spider was dangling over the table.

_____ **15.** It feels good to get up on a breezy spring morning.

_____ **16.** During a thunderstorm, it's safer to be inside than out.

_____ **17.** Rhyming games are fun to play at parties.

_____ **18.** Joan of Arc was one of the bravest women in history.

Dropping Silent *e* Before Adding a Suffix

1. The spelling of some root words is not changed before a suffix is added, as in *rugs.*

2. In some words, the final consonant is doubled before a suffix is added, as in *dragging.*

3. In some words, the final *y* is changed to *i* before a suffix is added, as in *prettiest.*

4. In most words with a final silent *e*, the *e* is dropped before a suffix is added, as in *moving.*

On the first line in front of each word below, write the numeral of the sentence above that tells how the suffix was added. On the second line, write the root word.

____ _____ **1.** shady

____ _____ **2.** wedding

____ _____ **3.** peaceful

____ _____ **4.** scarred

____ _____ **5.** posters

____ _____ **6.** nutty

____ _____ **7.** abilities

____ _____ **8.** rapidly

____ _____ **9.** relating

____ _____ **10.** boldest

____ _____ **11.** jogging

____ _____ **12.** chilly

____ _____ **13.** satisfied

____ _____ **14.** ordinarily

____ _____ **15.** porches

____ _____ **16.** freezer

____ _____ **17.** knotted

____ _____ **18.** thirsty

____ _____ **19.** glider

____ _____ **20.** barrelful

____ _____ **21.** jealously

____ _____ **22.** heroes

____ _____ **23.** tanner

____ _____ **24.** chirping

____ _____ **25.** strained

____ _____ **26.** necessarily

____ _____ **27.** waded

____ _____ **28.** soared

____ _____ **29.** centuries

____ _____ **30.** faintly

____ _____ **31.** dripping

____ _____ **32.** giggled

____ _____ **33.** clumsiest

____ _____ **34.** milder

____ _____ **35.** clipping

____ _____ **36.** sturdiest

Each of these prefixes means "not": *in-, non-, dis-,* and *un-*. The spelling of *in-* is generally changed to *im-* before words that begin with *m, b* or *p*.

in | complete   non | living   dis | agree   un | welcome
im | patient

The prefixes *un-* and *dis-* can also mean "the opposite of" the word to which they are added.

un | cover   dis | connect

Complete each sentence below by adding one of the above prefixes to each incomplete word.

1. There are very few vegetables that Connie _____likes.

2. Miguel sent me a message written in _____visible ink.

3. The old coin was _____like any other I'd ever seen.

4. The campers could not drink the water because it was _____pure.

5. I was amazed when the magician made the elephant _____appear.

6. We arrived at the meeting late because we took an _____direct route.

7. Martha paid us an _____expected visit yesterday.

8. Pablo became _____patient when his car would not start.

9. If you _____agree with the new rule, tell me your reasons.

10. The train traveled _____stop from Washington, D.C., to New York City.

11. It is _____polite to eat food with a knife.

12. Gerry had only one _____correct answer on his test.

13. Pioneers are thrilled with thoughts of the _____known.

14. I do not like the taste of _____fat milk.

15. To me, believing in ghosts is _____sense.

16. The _____complete game will be finished next week.

17. How can I _____lock the door if I've lost the key?

18. Kevin was _____pleased with his science grade.

34

The prefix *fore-* means "in front." *fore* | *foot*	The prefix *sub-* means "under" or "below." *sub* | *way*
The prefix *pre-* means "before." *pre* | *pay*	The prefix *inter-* means "between" or "among." *inter* | *state*

Each sentence below contains a word with the prefix *fore-*, *pre-*, *sub-*, or *inter-*. Underline the word and draw a line after the prefix. Then write its definition on the line.

1. If you preheat the oven, it will be hot when you put in the cake.

_____

2. The preview of next week's show looked exciting.

_____

3. Temperatures in Florida are almost never subfreezing.

_____

4. The sun is not as hot in the forenoon as it is after twelve.

_____

5. The subsoil was rockier than the rich earth on the surface.

_____

6. These frozen vegetables have been precooked and need only to be warmed up.

_____

7. Can you foretell my future by reading my palm?

_____

8. A subtitle sometimes gives a clue to what a book is about.

_____

9. Most countries have strong laws about international trade.

_____

The prefix *mis-* means "wrong."	The prefix *re-* means "back" and "again."
mis	*print*	*re*	*paid* *re*	*build*

In the list below, circle each word in which *mis-* or *re-* is a
prefix. Underline the root word.

repay	mister	restart	replaced	misfortune
misty	recopy	misstep	misfired	misspelled
reprint	reader	reclaim	misjudged	repainted
reason	refill	recounted	relocated	misunderstand

Complete each sentence below by writing one of the words
circled above on the line.

1. Nick took the paint set from the shelf, checked the price, and quickly

   _____ it.

2. Once the car stopped, Lang could not _____ it.

3. A word is _____ on page seven of my math book.

4. The old man did not know how to _____ Charlene's kindness.

5. If you speak slowly, no one will _____ what you're saying.

6. Last summer, the schoolrooms were _____ a bright color.

7. After lunch, _____ the pitcher with more fruit punch.

8. The center fielder _____ the fly ball, and it dropped to the ground.

9. Lisa had to _____ her homework after it fell into a puddle.

10. Alfredo had the _____ of breaking his leg in a football game.

11. The farmer _____ the beehives farther from the house.

12. Wendy went to the bus station to _____ her lost coat.

13. If you take just one _____, you could easily fall from the roof.

14. When the pirate's cannon _____, the little ship escaped.

15. Bill _____ his change after he left the store.

Prefixes **mis-** and **re-**

Each of these suffixes means "the action of doing" or "the state of being": -ion, -sion, -ation, and -ition.

perfection   *persuasion*   *explanation*   *addition*

After each word below, write its root word. If necessary, use a dictionary to check the spelling.

1. prevention _____
2. observation _____
3. direction _____
4. exploration _____
5. suggestion _____

6. action _____
7. invitation _____
8. decoration _____
9. location _____
10. introduction _____

The suffix -ment means	The suffix -ness means
"the action of doing" *payment*	"the state of being" *darkness*
"the state of being" *accomplishment*	
"a thing that" *statement*	

Complete each sentence below by adding one of the suffixes on this page to the word at the beginning of the sentence. Write the new word on the line.

(settle) 1. Jamestown was the first _____ in this country.

(bright) 2. The sudden _____ of the sun hurt my eyes.

(protect) 3. A porcupine has excellent natural _____.

(add) 4. The Bowers family just put an _____ on their house.

(imagine) 5. Sometimes Vera lets her _____ run away with her.

(confuse) 6. The flood caused a lot of _____ in the town.

(improve) 7. Roni knows that her spelling needs _____.

(strange) 8. There was a _____ about the house that scared Ben.

(collect) 9. My brother has a large _____ of tapes and CDs.

(admire) 10. People have great _____ for President Lincoln.

The suffix *-ful* means		The suffix *-less* means	
"full of"	*careful*	"without"	*care**less***
"the amount that fills"	*cup**ful***		

Complete the paragraph below by writing *-ful* or *-less* on each line.

Have you ever thought about being trapped in a room_____ of panthers? What would you do if you had a house_____ of tigers? Can you imagine being in such a hope_____ situation? If you were the fear_____ Gunter Gebel-Williams, you'd have had no problem at all. You'd simply tell the growling but respect_____ cats to sit down. And they would! Gunther Gebel-Williams was the world's most famous animal trainer. He didn't work with tooth_____ old animals that couldn't hurt him. And his cats certainly weren't play_____ little kittens, either. Gebel-Williams trained power_____ panthers and tigers. They could have eaten him in a big mouth_____. One care_____ mistake by Gebel-Williams could mean pain_____ injuries or even death. He was a care_____ man, though. And that made him success_____. To his other traits, he added a huge cup_____ of courage. He always personally gave his cats food by the hand_____. So Gebel-Williams got to know them. He knew them well enough to wear a live leopard for a shawl! Gunther Gebel-Williams performed to the end_____ applause of circus fans all over the world.

Write each word with the suffix *-ful* in the correct column.

"full of"   **"the amount that fills"**

_____ _____   _____ _____

_____ _____   _____ _____

_____ _____   _____

Each of these suffixes means "a person who": *-er* and *-or.*

The suffix *-ist* also means "a person who." It tells that the person has something to do with the root word.

painter   *visitor*   *violinist*

Make a new word by adding *-er, -or,* or *-ist* to each word below. Write the new word on the line. It may be necessary to change the spelling of a root word before adding a suffix.

1. explore _____

2. art _____

3. report _____

4. science _____

5. box _____

6. speak _____

7. weave _____

8. act _____

9. special _____

10. swim _____

11. invent _____

12. entertain _____

Complete the crossword puzzle by using the new words above.

ACROSS

1. A _____ talks to someone else.
5. A _____ does particular tasks.
7. An _____ travels to unknown places.
8. An _____ makes up new things.
9. An _____ plays a part in the movies.
10. An _____ works with paintings.

DOWN

1. A _____ is an expert in facts.
2. An _____ performs for others in public.
3. A _____ makes rugs, baskets, etc.
4. A _____ gathers news.
5. A _____ moves through the water.
6. A _____ fights with fists for sport.

The suffixes *-able* and *-ible* mean "able to" and "able to be done."	The suffix *-al* means "of or belonging to" and "the action of."
accept**able** forc**ible**	comic**al** dismiss**al**

In the paragraph below, circle each word with the suffix *-able*, *-ible*, or *-al*.

Last weekend, I had a remarkable experience. My friends and I went bowling. Right after our arrival, we rented bowling shoes and went to our lane. Two older people came to the lane next to ours, and it was noticeable that the man was moving slowly and carefully. I soon realized that he was blind, but that was not recognizable at first. In a few moments, the two people were putting up a railing made of light metal. Then this admirable man began to bowl! To guide him down the alley, he ran his right hand along the railing. His shot was respectable even for a person who could see. I found out later that the man had been hurt as a young soldier. His personal refusal to let blindness slow him down was amazing. He had always liked bowling so it seemed natural and sensible to continue. His first railing was experimental, but now he and his wife go bowling regularly. They have also helped form a national group that supports other blind people who want to be active in sports.

List the root words of the circled words.

_____   _____   _____

_____   _____   _____

_____   _____   _____

_____   _____   _____

The suffix -*y* means		The suffix -*ly* means	
"like"	*stormy*	"like"	*brotherly*
"full of"	*salty*	"each" or "every"	*yearly*
"the state of being"	*jealousy*	"in a way that is"	*quietly*

Complete each sentence below by adding -*y* or -*ly* to a word in the WORD BOX.

WORD BOX

rock	soap	swamp	snow	difficult
home	night	perfect	silent	week
loud	fish	shy	honest	friend

1. The old wooden dock had a _____ smell.

2. Juan used a bucket of _____ water to clean the car.

3. The beautiful butterfly perched _____ on the flower.

4. Yoko eagerly awaits her _____ paycheck each Friday.

5. The little log cabin was very _____ inside.

6. Tracy smiled _____ for the camera.

7. The fireworks thundered _____ and lit up the sky.

8. Some TV shows are on _____ and some only once a week.

9. With much _____, Brett used crutches to climb the stairs.

10. I always like to be the first person to walk through a _____ field.

11. Pat gave me a _____ smile when we were introduced.

12. The _____ path made hiking difficult.

13. Sue showed her _____ when she returned the lost wallet to its owner.

14. After the heavy rains, the field was too _____ to walk through.

15. Kelly imitates _____ the calls made by different birds.

The suffix *-ish* means			The suffix *-ous* means	
"like"	*childish*		"like"	*bulbous*
"somewhat"	*brownish*		"full of"	*glorious*

Circle the suffix in each word below. Then write the root word on the line.

1. mysterious _____
2. smallish _____
3. poisonous _____
4. dangerous _____
5. wolfish _____
6. sickish _____

7. adventurous _____
8. humorous _____
9. marvelous _____
10. famous _____
11. pinkish _____
12. tallish _____

Complete each sentence below with one of the words from the list above.

1. After not eating all day, Zach had a _____ hunger.

2. A sign warned drivers of a _____ curve in the road ahead.

3. Just before sunset the sky glowed with a beautiful _____ color.

4. Be sure to keep _____ items out of the reach of small children.

5. Our new car is _____ and doesn't use much gas.

6. The _____ noise outside our tent kept us awake all night.

7. We laughed at the _____ story Mr. Wilson told.

8. The _____ people should stand in the back row, not the front.

9. The astronauts returned safely from their _____ trip into space.

10. Sometimes I daydream about being a _____ model.

11. The way the team came from behind and won was _____.

12. Ms. Newton still felt _____ after she came home from the hospital.

Prefixes		Suffixes		
in-, im-, dis-, un- sub-		-ion, -sion, -ation, -ition	-y, -ly	-less
pre- inter-		-er, -or	-ment	-ist
fore- re-		-able, -ible	-ness	-al
mis-		-ous	-ful	-ish

Complete each sentence by adding one of the above prefixes to the word given below each line.

1. I find it a help to _____ my work for each coming week.
(plan)

2. Wu Fan bumped his _____ on the car door.
(head)

3. The _____ disappeared into a dark tunnel.
(way)

4. I will not be able to _____ you until next week.
(pay)

5. Large _____ highways connect the Atlantic and Pacific coasts.
(state)

6. Please do not _____ any of the library books.
(use)

7. Friends can _____ with each other and still be friends.
(agree)

Complete each sentence below by adding one of the suffixes listed at the top of the page to the word given below each line.

1. The _____ filled the bottle with red pills.
(drug)

2. Tiana's _____ kept her home for ten days.
(ill)

3. My latest _____ seems to be working.
(invent)

4. The rug will not fit unless the _____ of the room is correct.
(measure)

5. The _____ vase fell and is now in hundreds of pieces.
(break)

6. The _____ radioed his position to the Coast Guard.
(sail)

7. Fog has caused the late _____ of John's plane.
(arrive)

Prefixes		Suffixes		
in-, im-, dis-, un-	*sub-*	*-ion, -sion, -ation, -ition*	*-y, -ly*	*-less*
pre-	*inter-*	*-er, -or*	*-ment*	*-ist*
fore-	*re-*	*-able, -ible*	*-ness*	*-al*
mis-		*-ous*	*-ful*	*-ish*

In the paragraph below, circle each word containing one of the above prefixes or suffixes.

Size is a very unusual thing. Sometimes I feel quite large. At other times I feel rather smallish. Let me explain so you don't misunderstand. I feel like a huge building next to a small ant. But next to a giant oak tree, I feel little. Do you think the world is huge? It would not be exactly truthful for me to say it is. The earth is quite small. Next to our planet, the sun is a giant. Even though the sun looks almost reachable, it is 92 million miles away. So if you thought the sun was little, you were incorrect. But maybe you should reconsider. Would you disbelieve me now if I said the sun was tiny? In all honesty, it is when compared to other stars! Yet even the biggest star is small in the endless space. Now lean your forehead on your hand and give some thought to size.

On each line below, write one of the circled words and another word containing the same prefix or suffix.

1. _____

2. _____

3. _____

4. _____

5. _____

6. _____

7. _____

8. _____

Review Prefixes and Suffixes

Underline the prefixes and the suffixes in the words below.
Then write the root words on the lines.

1. discontinue _____

2. noticeable _____

3. subhuman _____

4. traveler _____

5. stylish _____

6. observation _____

7. mispronounce _____

8. fearless _____

9. interstate _____

10. jealousy _____

11. confusion _____

12. unaware _____

13. youthful _____

14. repack _____

15. scarcely _____

16. foresee _____

17. childish _____

18. collector _____

19. violinist _____

20. humorous _____

21. incomplete _____

22. protection _____

23. juicy _____

24. painless _____

25. preview _____

26. natural _____

27. eagerness _____

28. nonsense _____

29. impatient _____

30. addition _____

31. payment _____

32. forenoon _____

33. sensible _____

34. unequal _____

35. nonbreakable _____

36. unselfish _____

37. subtropical _____

38. indirectly _____

39. forecaster _____

40. disrespectful _____

41. interaction _____

42. immovable _____

In the paragraph below, underline each word that has one of
these prefixes or suffixes.

Prefixes — *in-, im-, dis-, un-, pre-, fore-, mis-, sub-, inter-, re-*
Suffixes — *-ion, -sion, -ation, -ition, -ment, -ness, -ful, -less,*
-er, -or, -ist, -able, -ible, -al, -y, -ly, -ish, -ous

I was impatiently awaiting the arrival of our vacation. It
was going to be my first trip to the ocean. We left at dawn
one July morning. There was no confusion. We had
finished packing the night before. As soon as I got in the
car, my imagination started working. The pictures in my
mind were like a movie preview. First I thought of the
foamy waves crashing onto the beach. Then I thought of
the uneven stretch of sand. I imagined the boardwalk.
Often I stopped the action in my mind. Then I could look
at it like a picture that an artist had painted. It was all so
marvelous! I even thought of being a sailor on a
submarine. I only discontinued my daydreaming when we
got to the shore. To my surprise, I found my dreams had
been incomplete. The beach and the ocean were more
beautiful than I had thought. Even though I'm home
again, I'm still a daydreamer. Now I replay in my mind
movies of the good time I really had.

Write the root word for each underlined word above.

1. _____   7. _____   13. _____

2. _____   8. _____   14. _____

3. _____   9. _____   15. _____

4. _____   10. _____   16. _____

5. _____   11. _____   17. _____

6. _____   12. _____   18. _____

On each line below, write the contraction formed by the two words.

1. they will _____
2. she is _____
3. I am _____
4. what is _____
5. we had _____

6. there is _____
7. he has _____
8. they are _____
9. you have _____
10. do not _____

Draw a line to connect the words that form a compound word.
Then write the new compound word on the line.

spring	print	1. _____
ever	sight	2. _____
eye	spoon	3. _____
week	born	4. _____
home	time	5. _____
foot	made	6. _____
sun	end	7. _____
new	green	8. _____
tea	rise	9. _____

Rewrite each phrase to show possession.

1. the room of the guests _____
2. the park of the children _____
3. the scales of a butcher _____
4. the tricks of the dolphins _____
5. the treasure of a pirate _____
6. the necks of the oxen _____
7. the instruments of the musicians _____
8. the spacesuit of an astronaut _____
9. the whiskers of the mice _____

1. The spelling of some words is not changed before a suffix is added.
2. In some words, the final consonant is doubled before a suffix is added.
3. In some words, the final *y* is changed to *i* before a suffix is added.
4. In most words with a final silent *e,* the *e* is dropped before a suffix is added.

On the line in front of each word, write the numeral of the sentence above that tells how the ending was added to the word. On the line after each word, write its root word.

____ **1.** abilities _____

____ **2.** thriller _____

____ **3.** boiled _____

____ **4.** foggy _____

____ **5.** smokiest _____

____ **6.** dozing _____

____ **7.** supplies _____

____ **8.** soapy _____

____ **9.** hissing _____

____ **10.** envied _____

____ **11.** gripping _____

____ **12.** juicy _____

____ **13.** winner _____

____ **14.** tamest _____

After each word, write its word parts in the correct column.

	Prefix	Root Word	Suffix
1. impatiently	_____	_____	_____
2. returnable	_____	_____	_____
3. unlikeable	_____	_____	_____
4. misstatement	_____	_____	_____
5. disorderly	_____	_____	_____
6. international	_____	_____	_____
7. unsuccessful	_____	_____	_____
8. refinisher	_____	_____	_____
9. nonpoisonous	_____	_____	_____
10. dislocation	_____	_____	_____

Each syllable in a word contains one vowel sound. To find out the number of syllables in a word, count the number of vowel sounds that are heard.

Below each picture, write the numeral that tells how many syllables are heard in the picture name.

      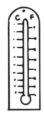      

_____   _____   _____   _____   _____

_____   _____   _____   _____   _____

On each line write the numeral that tells how many syllables are heard in the word.

____ 1. roam	____ 11. discovery	____ 21. vinegar	____ 31. kennel
____ 2. librarian	____ 12. necessary	____ 22. rhyme	____ 32. geography
____ 3. area	____ 13. skeleton	____ 23. doubt	____ 33. improvement
____ 4. olive	____ 14. envelope	____ 24. heaven	____ 34. pronunciation
____ 5. uneasily	____ 15. wheat	____ 25. lonely	____ 35. experience
____ 6. bruise	____ 16. festival	____ 26. forever	____ 36. responsibility
____ 7. hamburger	____ 17. society	____ 27. ache	____ 37. unexpected
____ 8. pause	____ 18. forehead	____ 28. kneel	____ 38. journey
____ 9. territory	____ 19. oxygen	____ 29. elegant	____ 39. conversation
____ 10. gradual	____ 20. poet	____ 30. throughout	____ 40. imagination

1. If a word contains a double consonant, divide **between** the double consonant.

spar | row

2. If two unlike consonants come between two vowels, divide **between** the consonants.

lan | tern

3. If a consonant comes between two vowels and the first vowel is short, divide **after** the consonant.

liz | ard

4. If a consonant comes between two vowels and the first vowel is long, divide **before** the consonant.

pu | pil

5. If a word ends in *le* and a consonant comes before *le*, divide **before** the consonant.

an | kle

6. If two vowels come together in a word and each vowel stands for one sound, divide **between** the vowels.

li | on

On the line in front of each word, write the numeral of the sentence that tells how the word is divided. Then draw a line to divide the word into syllables.

____ **1.** cabin

____ **2.** tunnel

____ **3.** jungle

____ **4.** silence

____ **5.** twenty

____ **6.** shiver

____ **7.** cruel

____ **8.** jingle

____ **9.** flutter

____ **10.** trial

____ **11.** patient

____ **12.** captain

____ **13.** metal

____ **14.** private

____ **15.** cider

____ **16.** native

____ **17.** sample

____ **18.** canyon

____ **19.** cocoa

____ **20.** legend

____ **21.** giant

____ **22.** tangle

____ **23.** salad

____ **24.** costume

____ **25.** collapse

____ **26.** future

____ **27.** velvet

____ **28.** clipper

____ **29.** column

____ **30.** sprinkle

____ **31.** science

____ **32.** bamboo

____ **33.** poet

____ **34.** success

____ **35.** human

____ **36.** marble

____ **37.** clumsy

____ **38.** monarch

____ **39.** tremble

____ **40.** soda

1. Words that contain a consonant blend or a consonant digraph are usually not divided between the letters that make up the blend or digraph.

 ze | bra

 bu<u>ck</u> | et

2. If a prefix or a suffix is added to a root word, it usually forms a separate syllable.

 <u>un</u> | lock

 sail | <u>or</u>

3. In a compound word, divide between the words that make up the compound word.

 bee | hive

On the line in front of each word below, write the numeral of the sentence above that tells how the word is divided. (Sometimes more than one numeral could be used.) Then divide the word into syllables. On the line after the word, write the letter of the correct definition.

____ **1.** preview ____

____ **2.** airport ____

____ **3.** dreadful ____

____ **4.** panther ____

____ **5.** highway ____

____ **6.** replace ____

____ **7.** drugstore ____

____ **8.** fluffy ____

____ **9.** rancher ____

____ **10.** merchant ____

a. A place where medicine is sold

b. Terrible

c. A black leopard

d. A person who raises cattle, sheep, or horses

e. Soft and light

f. To put back

g. A person who buys and sells goods

h. A place where planes land and take off

i. To see ahead of time

j. A main road

Syllabication

Divide the words in each group into syllables. On the line in front of each word, write the numeral of the word in the box that is divided in the same way. (Sometimes more than one numeral could be used.)

1. Double consonants—*mit | ten*
2. Unlike consonants—*hun | ger*
3. Short vowel/consonant/vowel—*rap | id*
4. Long vowel/consonant/vowel—*ci | der*
5. Consonant before *le*—*mar | ble*
6. Between two vowels—*po | et*

____ 1. habit	____ 9. runner	____ 17. castle
____ 2. collect	____ 10. dial	____ 18. certain
____ 3. couple	____ 11. beaver	____ 19. crayon
____ 4. label	____ 12. timber	____ 20. lemon
____ 5. member	____ 13. finish	____ 21. riot
____ 6. heaven	____ 14. creature	____ 22. puzzle
____ 7. real	____ 15. beyond	____ 23. cover
____ 8. turtle	____ 16. bacon	____ 24. picnic

7. Blend or digraph—*pro | gram, thick | et*
8. Prefix or suffix—*un | like, wood | en*
9. Compound word—*bull | dog*

____ 1. sunshine	____ 9. disgrace	____ 17. pancake
____ 2. lonely	____ 10. nowhere	____ 18. orchard
____ 3. prefix	____ 11. mouthful	____ 19. speechless
____ 4. daylight	____ 12. somehow	____ 20. railroad
____ 5. leafy	____ 13. flashlight	____ 21. eyebrow
____ 6. redo	____ 14. breathless	____ 22. unload
____ 7. twister	____ 15. bushel	____ 23. windshield
____ 8. schoolroom	____ 16. firefly	____ 24. misspell

Review Syllabication

To alphabetize words that begin with the same letter or letters, find the first letter in each word that is different. Then put the words in alphabetical order according to these letters.

n**o**rth ⎫ nail
n**a**il ⎬ neck
n**i**ght ⎪ night
n**e**ck ⎭ north

Number the words in each group in alphabetical order.

___ dozen	___ leave	___ trainer	___ forty
___ dolphin	___ lean	___ trail	___ forth
___ dock	___ learn	___ track	___ formed
___ doubt	___ leash	___ trains	___ fortune

Complete the alphabetical list below with the words in the WORD BOX.

———— WORD BOX ————

goldfish	jingle	imagine	backyard
disappear	quarrel	visible	often
office	operate	quarter	young
imitate	disease	golden	immediate
operator	background	jigsaw	visitor

1. _____

2. backward

3. _____

4. _____

5. disappoint

6. _____

7. disgrace

8. _____

9. _____

10. imaginary

11. imagination

12. _____

13. _____

14. _____

15. jiggle

16. _____

17. _____

18. offer

19. _____

20. official

21. _____

22. open

23. _____

24. _____

25. opinion

26. quack

27. _____

28. _____

29. violin

30. _____

31. _____

32. _____

33. youth

Dictionary—Alphabetical Order

53

Think of a dictionary as having three parts: front, middle, and back.

Front
Words beginning with
a, b, c, d, e, f, and *g*

Middle
Words beginning
with *h, i, j, k, l,*
m, n, o, and *p*

Back
Words beginning with
q, r, s, t, u, v, w, x, y,
and *z*

When looking for a word in a dictionary, decide which part it is in. Then open the dictionary to that part. This method will save time in looking for a word.

In which part of a dictionary are the following words found? On each line, write *front, middle,* or *back.*

1. moan _____

2. web _____

3. canary _____

4. quiver _____

5. former _____

6. kettle _____

7. zipper _____

8. alert _____

9. navy _____

10. tickle _____

11. gesture _____

12. seek _____

13. barge _____

14. van _____

15. kangaroo _____

16. pinch _____

17. harvest _____

18. dignity _____

19. yelp _____

20. law _____

21. olive _____

In a dictionary, words are listed in alphabetical order.

Write in alphabetical order five more words that would be found in each section of a dictionary.

Front	**Middle**	**Back**
_____	_____	_____
_____	_____	_____
_____	_____	_____
_____	_____	_____
_____	_____	_____

Dictionary—Three Parts, Alphabetical Order

The two heavy dark words at the top of a dictionary page are called *guide words*. The one on the left tells the first word on a page. The one on the right tells the last word on a page. Words that come alphabetically between the two guide words are found on that page.

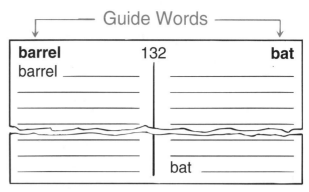

| tape | 606 | teach | teacher | 607 | tell |
| table | 604 | tale | talk | 605 | tap |

Look at the guide words for the four dictionary pages shown above. On each line, write the numeral of the page on which the word is found.

_____ **1.** tank	_____ **6.** tea	_____ **11.** task	_____ **16.** tangle
_____ **2.** team	_____ **7.** tack	_____ **12.** tan	_____ **17.** tailor
_____ **3.** tag	_____ **8.** taught	_____ **13.** taxi	_____ **18.** teeth
_____ **4.** tasty	_____ **9.** tame	_____ **14.** tail	_____ **19.** taste
_____ **5.** tall	_____ **10.** tear	_____ **15.** tease	_____ **20.** taken

After each pair of guide words, underline the words that would appear on that page.

1. ledge—lid	leave	lie	level	lift
2. vein—vine	van	view	violin	village
3. ill—inch	immediate	impatient	indeed	idea
4. dough—drawn	dream	doubt	dozen	dragon
5. east—effort	eaten	edge	ease	effect
6. modern—month	moment	monkey	mood	model
7. north—now	notch	noon	nowhere	notice
8. pole—porch	poke	port	poppy	polite
9. quarrel—quick	quart	question	quack	quite
10. grape—green	great	grand	greet	grasp

The words defined in a dictionary are called *entry words*. They are always listed alphabetically. Usually they are also written in dark type and divided into syllables.

Entry Word →

poke (pōk), **1.** to push a person or thing with something pointed: *She poked herself with a pencil.* **2.** to push or pry into things: *Don't poke into other people's business.* **3.** a pushing or poking. **4.** to move in a slow, lazy way: *Jeff poked on his way to school.* 1, 2, 4 *verb,* **poked, pok•ing;** 3 *noun.*

pol•ka (pōl´ kə or pō´ kə), **1.** a lively dance. **2.** the music for this dance. *noun, plural* **pol•kas.**

prowl (proul), **1.** to move about quietly and secretly as if hunting for something. **2.** to wander. **3.** a prowling. 1, 2 *verb,* 3 *noun.*

quart (kwôrt), **1.** a liquid measure equal to one fourth of a gallon: *a quart of oil.* **2.** a dry measure equal to one eighth of a peck: *a quart of strawberries. noun.*

Queens (kwēnz), a borough of New York City, east of Brooklyn on Long Island. *noun.*

quiv•er¹ (kwĭv´ər), **1.** to shake; to tremble: *Although the man escaped from the burning house, he still quivered in fear.* **2.** a shaking or trembling: *The quiver of the tree branch startled me.* 1 *verb,* 2 *noun.*

quiv•er² (kwĭv´ ər), a case for holding arrows. *noun.*

race•track (rās´ trăk), a round or oval area of ground laid out for racing. *noun.*

rat (răt), **1.** a gnawing animal that looks like a mouse but is larger, with gray, brown, black, or white fur. **2.** a mean person. *noun.*

read•er (rē´ dər), **1.** a person who reads. **2.** a book for learning or practicing reading. *noun.*

reef (rēf), a ridge of rocks or sand at or near the surface of the water. *noun.*

re•mark•a•ble (rĭ mär´ kə bəl), worthy of being noticed, unusual: *The new sculpture in front of the museum is remarkable. adjective.*

Entry Word

---

1. How many entry words are shown? _____

2. How many entry words begin with *q*? _____

3. How many entry words have only one syllable? _____

4. Which entry word has four syllables? _____

5. Which entry word begins with a capital letter? _____

6. Which entry words have endings added to them? _____

7. Which entry word is a compound word? _____

8. Which spelling has two entries? _____

9. Which entry word has two pronunciations? _____

Not all words are listed as entry words in a dictionary. If endings or suffixes have been added to words, the words are often included with the entry of the root word.

• •

ac•cuse (ə kyüz´), to blame for being or doing something wrong: *Our neighbors accused me of breaking the window.* verb, **ac•cused, ac•cus•ing.**

cen•tur•y (sĕn´ chər ē), a period of 100 years. *noun, plural* **cen•tur•ies.**

child (chīld), **1.** a baby. **2.** a young boy or girl. **3.** a son or daughter. *noun, plural* **chil•dren.**

eat (ēt), **1.** to chew and swallow food. **2.** to have a meal: *We ate at six o'clock.* **3.** to wear away; to destroy; *The rust ate a hole in the bottom of the car door.* verb, **ate, eat•en, eat•ing.**

• •

The words below may not be listed as entry words in a dictionary. On the line after each one, write the entry word that would include it.

1. freer _____

2. located _____

3. trimmest _____

4. quitting _____

5. waddled _____

6. abilities _____

7. fittest _____

8. heroes _____

9. readier _____

10. mapped _____

11. expresses _____

12. boring _____

13. unhappier _____

14. rarest _____

15. imitated _____

16. owing _____

17. drier _____

18. confused _____

19. noticing _____

20. youths _____

21. blamed _____

22. jolliest _____

23. circled _____

24. dozing _____

25. separated _____

26. valleys _____

27. oldest _____

28. measuring _____

29. kidded _____

30. overgrowing _____

In a dictionary, the pronunciation of each word is shown in parentheses after the entry word. The letters or symbols used represent the sound heard in the word. The short pronunciation key below is like the one found in a dictionary.

───── Pronunciation Key ─────

ă cat	ā cake	ä father	ch chin	ĕ red	ē see	ėr her
g get	ĭ big	ī ride	j jump	ng ring	ŏ stop	ō hope
ô talk	oi noise	ou out	s sit	sh shall		th thank
ŦH then	ŭ cut	u̇ put	ü rule	yü cute		zh pleasure
ə about, spoken, giraffe, police, picture				z rose		

After each respelling below, write the key word from the pronunciation key above that tells how the underlined letter or letters are pronounced.

1. chōz _____

2. dout _____

3. rông _____

4. grĭp _____

5. hĕlth _____

6. nŏt _____

7. ēz _____

8. flăp _____

9. ŦHō _____

10. rĭj _____

11. hu̇d _____

12. sēl _____

13. jüs _____

14. blėrt _____

15. dŭsk _____

16. pān _____

17. kyüb _____

18. trăsh _____

19. lĕft _____

20. hôk _____

21. rīm _____

22. chois _____

23. mŭg _____

24. ärch _____

Use the pronunciation key to decide which respelling tells how to pronounce the word at the left. Circle the correct respelling.

1. **ghost**	jōst	fōst	gōst	gŏst
2. **ache**	āch	āk	ăk	ăch
3. **height**	hāt	hĕft	hīt	hĭt
4. **scene**	skēn	sān	sĕn	sēn
5. **lodge**	lŏg	lōg	lŏj	lŏch

58

Every dictionary includes in its pronunciation key a symbol that looks like an upside down *e*. This symbol is called a *schwa*. It stands for the vowel sound often heard in a syllable that is not stressed. Each vowel can have the sound of the schwa. The pronunciation key gives words to help pronounce it.

sofa
sō′ fə

barrel
băr′ əl

dolphin
dŏl′ fən

anchor
ăng′ kər

column
kŏl′ əm

In each word below, underline the vowel that stands for the schwa sound.

1. upper
2. purpose
3. wizard
4. council
5. doubtful

6. tailor
7. temper
8. zebra
9. perform
10. canyon

11. disease
12. success
13. siren
14. effect
15. capture

16. bacon
17. support
18. ashore
19. fossil
20. canoe

On the line in front of each respelling, write the letter of its word.

____ 1. plā′ ər   a. perform
____ 2. prə nouns′   b. persuade
____ 3. pān′ tər   c. partner
____ 4. pärt′ nər   d. player
____ 5. pĕb′ əl   e. purpose
____ 6. pər fôrm′   f. pattern
____ 7. păt′ ərn   g. provide
____ 8. pər swād′   h. painter
____ 9. prə vīd′   i. pronounce
____ 10. pėr′ pəs   j. pebble

____ 11. sə lüt′   a. sample
____ 12. shĕp′ ərd   b. sputter
____ 13. sə plī′   c. shelter
____ 14. stub′ ərn   d. salute
____ 15. săm′ pəl   e. simple
____ 16. shĕl′ tər   f. supply
____ 17. shŭf′ əl   g. shuffle
____ 18. spŭt′ ər   h. symbol
____ 19. sĭm′ pəl   i. stubborn
____ 20. sĭm′ bəl   j. shepherd

If a word has more than one syllable, one of the syllables is usually stressed more than the others. In a dictionary, an accent mark (′) is placed next to the syllable with the most stress.

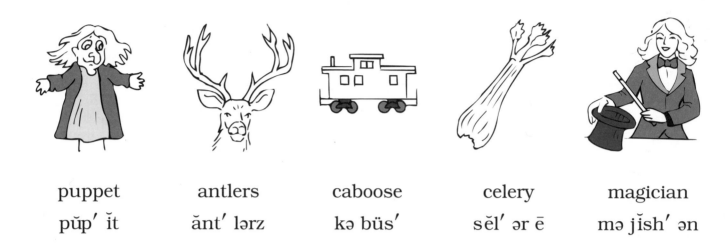

puppet	antlers	caboose	celery	magician
pŭp′ ĭt	ănt′ lərz	kə büs′	sĕl′ ər ē	mə jĭsh′ ən

Each word below is divided into syllables. Put an accent mark after the syllable with the most stress.

1. im prove

2. kan ga roo

3. mod ern

4. a corn

5. vol ca no

6. bam boo

7. de vel op

8. med i cal

9. fau cet

10. sat el lite

11. pro nounce

12. en ter tain

13. pi o neer

14. wis dom

15. ex am ine

16. op po site

17. com mit tee

18. de fend

19. pat tern

20. to ma to

21. grad u al

On the first line in front of each word, write the numeral that tells how many syllables are heard in it. On the second line, write the numeral of the syllable with the most stress.

____ ____ 1. disappoint

____ ____ 2. journey

____ ____ 3. imitate

____ ____ 4. interrupt

____ ____ 5. musician

____ ____ 6. accept

____ ____ 7. messenger

____ ____ 8. useless

____ ____ 9. foreign

____ ____ 10. introduce

____ ____ 11. pacific

____ ____ 12. hesitate

60

In words with more than one syllable, often more than one syllable is stressed. In a dictionary, a dark accent mark (ˈ) is placed next to the syllable with the most stress. A light accent mark (ˌ) is placed next to the syllable which is also stressed but not as much.

alligator
ăl′ ə gā′ tər

flashlight
flăsh′ līt′

Each word below is divided into syllables. Put a dark accent mark (ˈ) after the syllable with the most stress. Put a light accent mark (ˌ) after the syllable which is also stressed but not as much.

1. hand writ ing

2. bas ket ball

3. far a way

4. un dis turbed

5. vi o lin

6. moon light

7. eye brow

8. pi o neer

9. rec tan gle

10. in for ma tion

11. ham burg er

12. rep re sent

13. frame work

14. dec o rate

15. en ter tain

16. no bod y

17. an ces tor

18. con ver sa tion

19. card board

20. ant eat er

21. sit u a tion

22. es ca la tor

23. dic tion ar y

24. nec es sar y

The phonetic respellings of some of the above words are given below. Add both the dark and light accent marks to each one. Then write the normal spelling on the line.

1. rĕp ri zĕnt _____

2. kärd bôrd _____

3. ĕn tər tān _____

4. hăm bėr gər _____

5. nĕs ə sĕr ē _____

6. ī brou _____

7. pī ə nĭr _____

8. dĭk shə nėr ē _____

9. rĕk tăng gəl _____

10. frām wėrk _____

11. kŏn vər sā shən _____

12. ăn sĕs tər _____

Read the pairs of words below. Notice the shift of accent in the word with the suffix. When the suffix *-al, -ial, -ic, -ical, -ian, -ious,* or *-ity* is added to a word, the primary accent shifts to the syllable before the suffix.

mu′ sic   mu si′ cian   her′ o   he ro′ ic

The shift of accent in a word with a suffix often results in a vowel change.

po′ et (pō′ ĭt)   po et′ ic (pō ĕt′ ĭk)

col′ o ny (kŏl′ ə nē)   co lo′ ni al (kə lō′ nē əl)

Each word below is divided into syllables. Put a dark accent mark after the syllable with the most stress. Then circle any vowel that sounds different when the suffix is added and the accent shifts.

1. e qual	e qual i ty	9. mag net	mag net ic
2. mys ter y	mys ter i ous	10. cour age	cou ra geous
3. or i gin	o rig i nal	11. pres i dent	pres i den tial
4. mem or y	me mo ri al	12. li brar y	li brar i an
5. his tor y	his to ri cal	13. cur i ous	cur i os i ty
6. al pha bet	al pha bet i cal	14. mi cro scope	mi cro scop ic
7. ac ci dent	ac ci den tal	15. maj es ty	ma jes tic
8. ir ri gate	ir ri ga tion	16. e lec tric	e lec tric i ty

Complete each sentence below with a word from the WORD BOX.

—————————————— WORD BOX ——————————————

microscopic	electricity	irrigation	alphabetical
original	librarian	historical	mysterious

1. The _____ showed Max where the books about football were kept.

2. I arranged my video tapes in _____ order by title.

3. Many important events happened in the _____ town of Philadelphia.

4. The storm knocked out the _____ and left many homes with no heat.

5. Is this the _____ painting or a copy of it?

6. The dry desert was changed into rich, green farmland by _____.

7. These _____ germs are so small that you can't see them.

Sometimes a shift in accent changes the meaning of the word.

re•fuse[1] (rē fyüz′), **1.** to say no to something: *He refused to wear his boots.* **2.** to say one is not willing to do or give something: *They refused to accept the money. verb,* **re•fused, re•fus•ing.**

ref•use[2] (rĕf′ yüs), useless material; waste. *noun.*

Pronounce the pairs of words in the WORD BOX. Then complete each sentence below with one of the words. Include its accent mark.

```
_____ WORD BOX _____
```

pro duce′	pro test′	in crease′	con tent′
pro′ duce	pro′ test	in′ crease	con′ tent
sus pect′	per fect′	re cord′	ob ject′
sus′ pect	per′ fect	rec′ ord	ob′ ject

1. Dad does not _____ to my loud radio, but Mom does.

2. The _____ marchers carried signs in front of City Hall.

3. It takes many workers to _____ a new car.

4. On my birthday, I got an _____ in my allowance.

5. Doctors _____ that a virus causes the disease.

6. The inventor worked to _____ the machine.

7. The _____ of the car wash is to raise money for the band.

8. I play several bingo cards at once to _____ my chances of winning.

9. It did the player no good to _____ the umpire's call.

10. The _____ of some popular cereals is mainly sugar.

11. I think it's fun to _____ my voice on tape.

12. The police officer chased the _____ down the alley.

13. Not many people score a _____ 300 in bowling.

14. The _____ stand was full of fresh fruit and vegetables.

Dictionary—Accent Shift and Change of Meaning

ă cat   ā cake   ä father   ch chin   ĕ red   ē see   ėr her
g get   ĭ big   ī ride   j jump   ng ring   ŏ stop   ō hope
ô talk   oi noise   ou out   s sit   sh shall   th thank
ŦH then   ŭ cut   u̇ put   ü rule   yü cute   zh pleasure
ə about, spoken, giraffe, police, picture   z rose

Underline the respelling of the word that correctly completes each sentence.

1. Rosa used a (tăk, tāk, tŭk) to hang her drawing on the wall.

2. Corn, wheat, and rice are different kinds of (grēn, grān, grĭn).

3. It's dangerous to pull a (kär, shĕr, chĕr) out from under someone.

4. My older brother does not like to (lēnd, lănd, lĕnd) me his bike.

5. What's the difference between a (fėrm, färm, fôrm) and a ranch?

6. Andy wears (sēz, sĕz, sīz) seven shoes.

7. My family gave me a new (rŭb, rŏb, rōb) when I was in the hospital.

8. Ban Mo (thôt, tôt, ŦHō) we were leaving at nine o'clock.

9. The cold potatoes sat in a (lăm, lŭmp, lămp) on Colleen's plate.

10. It's a (sām, chŭm, shām) Dad didn't see your skateboard before moving the car.

11. Ramón likes to (wāk, wôk, wėrk) through the park on warm spring days.

12. We need three more points to (wŭn, wīn, wĭn) the championship.

Write the respelling of each word below.

1. did _____   6. eat _____

2. hat _____   7. not _____

3. step _____   8. duck _____

4. train _____   9. show _____

5. five _____   10. ice _____

Pronunciation Key

ă cat   ā cake   ä father   ch chin   ĕ red   ē see   ėr her
g get   ĭ big   ī ride   j jump   ng ring   ŏ stop   ō hope
ô talk   oi noise   ou out   s sit   sh shall   th thank
ŦH then   ŭ cut   u̇ put   ü rule   yü cute   zh pleasure
ə about, spoken, giraffe, police, picture   z rose

Complete each sentence with one of the respellings below it.

1. The northern _____ of the island was a wide, sandy beach.

kōst   gōst   chōz

2. Does this box _____ fossils or rocks?

kən fyüz′   kən fĕs′   kən tān′

3. The brothers often _____ over who will mow the lawn.

ə rōz′   är′ gyü   ə rĕst′

4. I can't understand what you say when you _____.

mŭm′ bəl   mŭs′ əl   măm′ əl

5. Do you _____ any of the new television shows?

ĕn′ jən   ĕn joi′   ĭn vent′

6. The cook added bananas to the delicious _____.

pu̇d′ l   pu̇d′ ĭng   pyü′ pəl

In front of each respelling below, write the letter of its definition.

____ **1.** mĕzh′ ər   **a.** A light rainfall

____ **2.** shăl′ ō   **b.** A person who lives in a small town

____ **3.** shou′ ər   **c.** To cover up with earth

____ **4.** bėr′ ō   **d.** Not deep

____ **5.** bĕr′ ē   **e.** A sour liquid

____ **6.** vĭn′ ə gər   **f.** A hole dug in the ground by an animal

____ **7.** vĭl′ ĭ jər   **g.** To find the size of something

Dictionary—Respellings   **65**

Many words have more than one meaning. In the dictionary, each separate meaning is numbered.

Read these dictionary entries for *bridge* and *hand*. Then read the sentences below. On the line, write the numeral of the definition that matches the use of the word in the sentence.

bridge (brĭj), **1.** a structure built over a road, river, or railroad: *The new bridge was opened to traffic yesterday.* **2.** an area above the deck of a ship for the commanding officer: *The captain watched the approaching storm from the bridge.* **3.** the upper bony part of the nose: *Her glasses kept sliding down over the bridge of her nose.* **4.** a mounting which holds false teeth attached to real teeth: *Mother's new bridge is not ready yet.* **5.** the movable piece over which the strings of a violin, cello, etc., are stretched: *The bridge of my violin broke just before my solo.* **6.** to make a way over something: *A log bridged the stream.* 1–5 *noun,* 6. *verb,* **bridged, bridg•ing.**

hand (hănd), **1.** the end part of the arm with four fingers and a thumb: *That glove is too big for my hand.* **2.** something that is like a hand: *the hands on a clock.* **3.** a paid worker: *a farm hand.* **4.** possession; control: *The matter is out of my hands.* **5.** a share in doing something: *I didn't have a hand in arranging the party.* **6.** side: *To my right hand is Mrs. Wang.* **7.** a handwriting style: *His letters are always in a dark, heavy hand.* **8.** skill: *He tried his hand at painting.* **9.** a promise to marry: *The prince asked for her hand.* **10.** the width of a hand; 4 inches: *A Shetland pony is about 9 hands high.* **11.** to give or pass with the hand: *Please hand me the salt.* **12.** to help with the hand: *The nurse handed the patient into a bed.* 1–10 *noun,* 11–12 *verb.*

For *bridge:*

_____ **1.** A thick board was used to bridge the gap between the rocks.

_____ **2.** The ball cracked my nose right at the bridge.

_____ **3.** The old covered bridge across that creek is falling down.

_____ **4.** The dentist fitted Granddad with a new bridge.

_____ **5.** After giving the signal to dive, the captain ran from the submarine bridge.

For *hand:*

_____ **6.** During summer vacation, Paul worked as a farm hand.

_____ **7.** "Happy Birthday" was written in a neat hand across the card.

_____ **8.** When playing gets out of hand, someone often gets hurt.

_____ **9.** The hands on Ricardo's watch glow in the dark.

_____ **10.** Mandy cannot throw a ball well with her left hand.

Homographs are words that are spelled alike but have different meanings. Sometimes they are pronounced differently, too. In a dictionary, homographs are listed as separate entry words with a small number placed after each one.

On the line in front of each sentence, write the numeral of the homograph used in that sentence. Do not write the numeral of the definition.

bark¹ (bärk), **1.** the outside covering of the trunk, branches, and roots of trees. **2.** to rub or scrape the skin off. 1 *noun,* 2 *verb.*

bark² (bärk), **1.** the short, loud noise made by a dog. **2.** to shout or speak loudly or gruffly. 1 *noun,* 2 *verb.*

____ **1.** All of the puppies in the pet shop began to bark at the same time.

____ **2.** The woodpecker tapped quickly through the bark to find its lunch.

____ **3.** Brian barked his knee when he fell on the sidewalk.

____ **4.** The coach barked loudly at the lazy members of the team.

file¹ (fīl), **1.** a folder, drawer, case, etc., for keeping papers and records in order. **2.** the papers or records kept in order. **3.** an orderly row of persons or things. **4.** to put in order. **5.** to march or move in an orderly way. 1–3 *noun,* 4–5 *verb,* **filed, fil•ing.**

file² (fīl), **1.** a steel tool with many small, sharp ridges or teeth to smooth or wear away hard materials. **2.** to smoooth or wear away with a file. 1 *noun,* 2 *verb,* **filed, fil•ing.**

____ **5.** Mom keeps her important papers in a file.

____ **6.** Stand in single file to wait for the bus.

____ **7.** It's better to file your fingernails than to bite them off.

____ **8.** The plumber used a file to smooth the end of the copper pipe.

tear¹ (tir), drop of salty liquid that keeps the eyeball moist. *noun.*

tear² (ter or târ), **1.** to pull apart by force. **2.** to make by ripping or pulling apart.

3. to cut deeply. **4.** to divide or split by opposite forces. **5.** to remove by force. **6.** to move with great haste. **7.** a torn place. 1–6 *verb,* **tore, torn, tear•ing;** 7 *noun.*

____ **9.** A huge crane will tear down the old post office today.

____ **10.** It will be easier to tear that paper if you fold it first.

____ **11.** A single tear rolled down the man's cheek.

____ **12.** When the saw began to tear into the thick tree trunk, wood chips went flying.

Homophones are words that sound alike but are spelled differently and have different meanings.

pare (pĕr or păr), **1.** to cut or shave off the outside part of something; to peel. **2.** to make smaller little by little. *verb.*

pear (pĕr or păr), **1.** a sweet fruit larger and more rounded at one end and smaller at the stem end. **2.** the tree on which this fruit grows. *noun.*

On each line, write a homophone for the word given.

1. oh _____

2. vein _____

3. peek _____

4. tied _____

5. heel _____

6. waste _____

7. board _____

8. pane _____

9. piece _____

10. mail _____

Read the paragraph below. On each line write one of the homophones given below it.

I have a new _____ of friends. Carlos
(pair, pear)

and his sister Isabel arrived _____ last
(here, hear)

_____ from Puerto Rico. They made the trip
(weak, week)

by _____. Each of them _____
(plain, plane)   (knows, nose)

how to _____ and _____ in
(read, reed)   (right, write)

both English and Spanish. Carlos and Isabel say that in Puerto Rico, the

weather is almost always _____. They have never even
(fair, fare)

_____ snow. Puerto Rico contains beautiful beaches,
(scene, seen)

mountains, and a _____ forest. Yet the
(rain, rein)

_____ island is _____ even as large as
(hole, whole)   (knot, not)

the state of Connecticut.

Synonyms are words that have the same, or almost the same, meaning.

Read the paragraphs below. In them, find a synonym for each numbered word. Write it on the line after the word.

1. game _____

2. start _____

3. big _____

4. view _____

5. similar _____

6. pretty _____

7. toss _____

8. rock _____

9. discovered _____

10. certain _____

11. looks _____

12. rush _____

13. yells _____

14. written _____

15. old _____

16. autumn _____

The game is about to begin. People fill the stands. The weather is mild, and the sky is beautiful. The large crowd shouts. Everyone watches as the players dash onto the field from a dark tunnel.

Does this sound like a football game on a fall afternoon? It could be. Or it could have happened in ancient Greece. In Greece, scientists have found the remains of a stadium more than 2,000 years old. They have learned that the stadiums of today and those of long ago are quite alike. However, some of the games are different. There were races and championship fights. One event was called the hammer throw. Another contest was held to see who could throw a spear farthest. The Greek people went to see their games just as modern fans do.

It was the stadium tunnel that most excited the scientists, though. On its stone walls, the Greek sports heroes had carved their names. The results of the events were recorded, too. So there's one thing that the scientists know for sure. Sports fans and players have not changed much during all these years.

Antonyms are words that have opposite meanings.

Read the paragraphs below. In them, find an antonym for each numbered word. Write it on the line after the word.

1. before _____

2. up _____

3. hot _____

4. bad _____

5. last _____

6. small _____

7. began _____

8. bottom _____

9. false _____

10. lost _____

11. lived _____

12. failed _____

13. low _____

14. easy _____

15. few _____

16. weak _____

Have you ever heard of the book *Around the World in Eighty Days?* In it, a man named Phineas Fogg travels around the world in a balloon. Many people who first read the story in 1873 thought it was true. However, it was just a good story.

That same year, 1873, marked the first time someone crossed the Atlantic Ocean in a balloon. Strong winds and bad weather ended that trip. Other people also tried, but the weather always won. Some of these travelers were lucky enough to get rescued from the cold water. But others died.

Finally, in 1978, three Americans succeeded in making the difficult journey. That was 105 years after the first try! The name of their large balloon was the Double Eagle II. It was 120 feet high. The top half was silver, and the rest was black. The men took off from the United States on a Friday. They came down almost six days later in France. Many people came to greet them. The good news flashed around the world.

chap¹ (chăp), **1.** to crack or open in slits: *My hands were chapped from the cold air.* **2.** to make rough: *The cold weather chapped his face. verb,* **chapped, chap•ping.**

chap² (chăp), a fellow; a man or boy. *noun.*

chart (chärt), **1.** a map, especially one that shows the coasts, rocks, reefs, currents, and depths of a sea. **2.** a sheet of information given in pictures, tables, lists, or diagrams. **3.** to make a chart: *The teacher charted the reading progress of each student.* 1–2 *noun,* 3 *verb.*

chick (chĭk), **1.** a young bird, especially a young chicken. **2.** a child. *noun.*

chim•pan•zee (chĭm′ păn′ zē or chĭm′ păn zē′), an intelligent African ape, not as large as a gorilla. *noun.*

chirp (chėrp), **1.** the short, quick sound made by some insects and small birds: *the chirp of a cricket.* **2.** to make this short, quick sound. 1 *noun,* 2 *verb.*

chunk (chŭngk), a short, thick piece or lump of something: *He cut the cheese into chunks. noun.*

churn (chėrn), **1.** a container in which butter is made from milk or cream by beating, stirring, or shaking. **2.** to beat, stir, or shake in a churn. **3.** to move as if being beaten, stirred, or shook: *My stomach was churning with hunger.* 1 *noun,* 2–3 *verb.*

cin•der (sĭn′ dər), **1.** a piece of partly burned wood or coal that may continue to burn but will no longer flame. **2.** completely burned wood or coal; ash. *noun.*

cit•y (sĭt′ ē), **1.** a large, important town, usually one that manages its own affairs: *Which city do you live closest to—San Francisco, Dallas, or Pittsburgh?* **2.** the people who live in a city: *As the city slept, it snowed and snowed.* **3.** of or in a city: *The city schools will open next week.* 1–2 *noun,* plural **cit•ies;** 3 *adjective.*

clum•sy (klŭm′ zē). **1.** not having skill or grace in moving; awkward: *The clumsy puppy tripped over the carpet.* **2.** not well made, well done, or well shaped: *The clumsy bookshelf could hold only a few books. adjective,* **clum•si•er, clum•si•est.**

---

1. What are the guide words on this page? _____

2. Circle the words that would come before this page.   chant   check   change

3. Circle the words that would come after this page.   clue   clutch   clung

4. How many entry words are shown? _____

5. Which spelling has two entries? _____

6. Which entry word has three syllables? _____

7. Which entry word has two pronunciations? _____

8. Under which entry word does *clumsier* appear? _____

9. Which entry words have the same vowel sound as *her?* _____

In each row, underline the synonym and circle the antonym of the first word.

1. bold	hot	cowardly	brave	few
2. defend	guard	lean	against	attack
3. future	past	hereafter	last	alone
4. mend	groan	crowd	destroy	repair
5. ordinary	usual	stop	rare	catch
6. sadness	fairness	sorrow	dryness	glee
7. rough	smooth	uneven	boat	fall
8. remain	forget	between	stay	depart
9. seldom	rarely	quiet	top	often
10. personal	none	public	private	young

In the first column below, write the homophone from the WORD BOX. In the second column, write the homograph for which two meanings are given.

WORD BOX

hose	people	noon	pear	brake
hail	pane	pupil	store	date
knot	note	heel	punch	mist
firm	juice	pure	mail	meal

1. pain _____

2. male _____

3. break _____

4. hoes _____

5. heal _____

6. not _____

7. missed _____

8. pare _____

9. solid _____

　　　a business

10. a student _____

　　　the black of an eye

11. to hit _____

　　　a sweet drink

12. a certain time _____

　　　a palm tree fruit